Writing MATHEMATICS

NANCY ROGERS BOSSE

Grade **1**

I saw this Pattern.

STAIRS FLAT STAIRS

Creative Publications

Edited by Rhea Irvine
Cover and text designed by Hyru Gau
Illustrations edited by Fred Geier
Coordinated by Theresa Tomlin
Composition by William Seabright & Associates

Thanks to the teachers and students who tried out these activities. Their work can be seen on pages iv-xi of this book.

© 1995 Creative Publications
1300 Villa Street
Mountain View, California 94041

Printed in the United States of America
ISBN: 1-56107-821-2
   3 4 5 6 7 8 9 10 99 98 97 96

Table of Contents

Notes to the Teacher

"To know mathematics is to engage in a quest to understand and communicate."

from NCTM Curriculum and Evaluation Standards for School Mathematics

WHAT IS *WRITING MATHEMATICS*?

Writing Mathematics is a series of resource books for grades one through six. Each book offers ten lessons designed to help children develop oral and written language as tools for learning and communicating mathematical ideas.

The key elements of the lessons ensure the active, social participation of children; the use of children's natural language and intuitive understandings; the connection of everyday language to the language of mathematics; and the development of children as writers of informal and structured expository writing. *Writing Mathematics* provides model experiences which can be incorporated throughout your mathematics program.

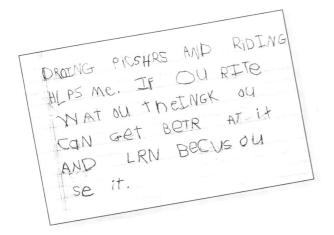

HOW IS *WRITING MATHEMATICS* ORGANIZED?

Included in *Writing Mathematics* are ten multi-day lessons which connect writing experiences to the investigation of key mathematical ideas.

The four-page guide to each lesson includes an overview, plans for the math investigation and writing extension, assessment criteria, and ideas for promoting discourse.

Use the Table of Contents to weave the *Writing Mathematics* lessons into your math outline for the year, or use the chart on page 1 to see how the lessons are intended to be used with *MathLand*.

WHAT ABOUT MANIPULATIVES?

The *Writing Mathematics* Manipulative Kit for Grade One (Cat. No 31851) includes the following materials:

1760 LinkerCubes in 7 colors
Thin Pattern Blocks, 144 of each shape
Pattern Block Stickers, one large set
40 orange Rainbow Tiles
Decahedra Dice, four sets
300 Teddy Bear Counters in two colors
35 Overhead Spinners

You may wish to have students or volunteers help with the preparation of manipulatives and classroom supplies prior to a lesson.

A Look Inside a Classroom

In this classroom, the children were engaged in the mathematics and writing lesson, *Our Favorites*. The mathematics investigation focused on collecting and organizing data about the children themselves. Children first made up three survey questions about favorites and drew pictures to answer them. They then invented many ways to sort the pictures and displayed them on posters.

The writing extension challenged the children to tell about the class's favorites by interpreting their posters. As the teacher recorded the children's ideas, she modeled writing mechanics and spelling. Writing their own sentences to report the class's favorites culminated the children's investigation into data. (See pages 2-5 for the complete lesson description.)

We found that kids like one cartoon the most. Zach

4 kids liked our second favorite cartoon. Sammy

We found out that 5 cartoons have animals. Alicia

A WORD ABOUT
WRITING TO LEARN

To learn mathematics, children must construct it for themselves. Constructing meaning engages children in many processes, including exploring, predicting, describing, debating, and justifying. Writing to report experiences, relate findings, and explain thinking, challenges children to use these same processes.

As children write to make sense of mathematics, they become aware of what they know and do not know. The motivation to increase their understanding is the product of their own process of making meaning. Awareness of their misconceptions helps children clarify their understandings, while consolidation of their understandings allows them to make connections and extend their thinking.

As the children explain and apply their understandings, teachers gain important insights into how each child is approaching and using mathematics.

"Math is a language that needs to be spoken; a music that needs to be heard; and an art that needs to be seen."

Rachel McAnallen

THE MATH INVESTIGATION

The investigation, *Our Favorites,* began with a discussion in which three categories of favorite things were chosen: cartoons, sports, and animals. Ownership of the investigation was immediately established because everyone had something to contribute. Each day the investigation focused on a different category, with the children following the same process of sorting and creating posters.

Throughout the investigation, the teacher observed and listened as each child brought something unique to the exploration. She was free to interact with the children, asking questions and challenging them to think in new ways.

THE WRITING EXTENSION

Following the math investigation, the children's interest in their favorites was naturally high. They contributed interpretations of the information on their posters to a class recording. To help the children formulate complete sentences, the teacher introduced the sentence starter, *We found out ___.* As she wrote the children's exact words on chart paper, she verbalized the process of writing sentences: *I'll make a capital W because it is the beginning of a sentence. ...I'll put a period to show it's the end of the sentence.*

Following the chart recording, the children were invited to write one fact for a class report about their favorites. In the writing below, the first child chose to copy word for word from the chart, while the other students used words and ideas from the chart to create their own sentences. Children have used their own spelling and that modeled on the chart.

Notice that the teacher accepted a variety of responses from the children, who didn't confine themselves to numerical comparisons of their favorites, but included other observations about the cartoons pictured in their posters.

A NOTE FROM A TEACHER

The children were eager to write about what they learned about the class favorites. At first their observations from the posters centered around the different types of favorites. With some encouragement and questioning, they began to make numerical observations from the posters such as, "Seven kids like playing on the bars and only two like playing in the fort best." It was also interesting to see their oral language develop as they listened to each other's statements.

Thinking out loud as I wrote what the children said was a very effective technique. I was pleased with how much the children put to use without a direct lesson so early in the year. Most of the children used words from the chart to express their own ideas.

A WORD ABOUT LEARNING TO WRITE

Throughout *Writing Mathematics*, children are engaged in the writing process and produce finished products for specific purposes and audiences.

Prewriting activities include investigating mathematics, holding discussions, and brainstorming. At the writing stage, children are presented with a structure with which to experiment as they write rough drafts. The variety of formats introduced support children as they write sentences, letters, directions, and reports to explain, convince, describe, compare, plan, and report.

The revision and editing stages involve children in rereading and rethinking the presentation of their ideas. Modeling, conferencing, peer editing, and using editing checklists help children approach this stage with confidence. Finally, the publication stage provides ways for children to share their writing for its planned purpose.

Initially, you will want to take children through the lessons step-by-step. As children become familiar with the writing process, they will work more independently and intermix the stages of writing, revising as they draft, for example.

Another Look Inside a Classroom

In this classroom, children were engaged in the mathematics and writing lesson, *Fences, Roads, and Walls.* The math investigation challenged the children to copy a motion pattern and then translate that pattern into other motions, sounds, and designs. Children used LinkerCubes and Pattern Blocks to show the patterns, and then recorded the patterns to later compare and discuss.

The writing extension continued the patterns exploration as the children were engaged in finding patterns in literature and around the school. The children recorded the patterns they found on a pattern hunt. The recordings were then used to look for ways their patterns were alike. (See the complete lesson description, pages 6-9.)

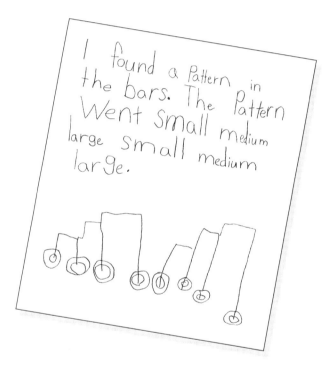

A WORD ABOUT CLASSROOM TALK

A feature appearing at the end of each lesson, *Classroom Talk*, touches upon the rationale for emphasizing oral language in the mathematics and writing curriculum, and provides helpful suggestions for promoting discourse in the classroom. Topics such as the link between oral language and writing, the role of silence in discourse, and the development of mathematical vocabulary are addressed.

Reading through all the *Classroom Talk* discussions prior to beginning *Writing Mathematics* is recommended; the suggestions provided are applicable throughout the program.

"Probing questions that encourage children to think and explain their thinking orally and in writing help them to understand more clearly the ideas they are expressing."

NCTM Curriculum and Evaluation Standards for School Mathematics

THE MATH INVESTIGATION

To begin the math sessions of *Fences, Roads, and Walls*, the teacher introduced the motion pattern *snap, clap, snap, clap*. Once everyone had joined in, she asked the children for another way to act out this pattern. After several of the children's suggestions were acted out, the children used LinkerCubes to show the pattern and talked about ways the pattern could be recorded. The investigation continued over several days as the children experimented with new patterns, new ways to act out the patterns, and new ways to record them.

THE WRITING EXTENSION

Back in the classroom after the pattern hunt, the children talked about the patterns they found. Their descriptions were recorded on chart paper, and sentence writing was modeled again.

With the chart paper recording and the sentence starter, *I found a pattern _____.* as models, the children drew pictures and then wrote sentences about the patterns they found.

In the samples shown above, the first child uses the sentence starter and expresses two complete thoughts. The second writer begins the sentence with original wording, is less clear about the structure of a sentence, and uses typical first-grade ingenuity to punctuate her sentence.

A NOTE FROM A TEACHER

My class enjoyed doing the math and the writing lesson, and I feel the students learned from their experiences. I was amazed at the ways the patterns were becoming more complex as the days progressed. Pairs working alongside each other would notice each other's work and stop to study it. After a while, I'd notice several pairs creating variations on the examined pattern.

I was especially pleased with how the children noticed other patterns throughout the day. One child noticed the pattern oto and cyc in the word motorcycle. Other students noticed a rock, hole, rock, hole pattern on the wall of a building on the way to lunch. These are the kinds of connections that show me learning has taken place.

A WORD ABOUT ASSESSMENT

Each lesson provides questions to think about while evaluating children's writing. The questions focus first on the children's thinking about mathematics and, second, on the children's use of the writing process and writing formats to communicate ideas. You may wish to use the questions as the framework for an assessment rubric.

The writing process provides many opportunities for self-assessment. Children reflect on their writing and use the responses of peers to evaluate and revise their writing. As children hear how their classmates have written, they have still another opportunity to reconsider the writing they have done.

To *MathLand* Teachers

Writing Mathematics is designed to be a supplement to the complete *MathLand* mathematics program. Teachers using *MathLand* already create mathematical environments which encourage children to think, to invent, to investigate, and to make connections.

Writing Mathematics provides exemplary writing extensions which add to the children's writing about thinking and self-assessment in *MathLand*. Some writing extensions are opportunities to take off from a *MathLand* investigation, while others provide a format for children to use as they do the writing called for within a *MathLand* investigation. Together, these experiences provide a rich program of learning to write and writing to learn.

The ten math investigations in *Writing Mathematics* provide synopses of investigations in the *MathLand* program. *MathLand* teachers will want to use the complete plans presented in the guidebook. It may be helpful to note in your guidebook the point of use for each writing extension, as shown in the chart below.

The techniques and writing formats provided in *Writing Mathematics* are intended to be used to extend other *MathLand* investigations; revisit these experiences as appropriate for your class.

Teachers not yet using *MathLand* and interested in this unique mathematics program are invited to call 800-357-MATH for information.

The *MathLand* • *Writing Mathematics* Correlation

MathLand			Writing Mathematics	
Unit 1	Week 2	Pages 16 - 19	Our Favorites	Pages 2 - 5
Unit 2	Week 1	Pages 32 - 35	Fences, Roads, and Walls	Pages 6 - 9
Unit 3	Week 4	Pages 80 - 81	Toss and Make	Pages 10 - 13
Unit 4	Week 2	Page 115	How Many Outfits?	Pages 14 - 17
Unit 5	Week 5	Pages 160 - 163	Upstairs, Downstairs	Pages 18 - 21
Unit 6	Week 1	Pages 176 - 177	Teddy and Me	Pages 22 - 25
Unit 7	Week 1	Pages 208 - 211	Bears on the Bus	Pages 26 - 29
Unit 8	Week 1	Page 261	Number Switch	Pages 30 - 33
Unit 9	Week 1	Pages 304 - 305	I Spy a Shape	Pages 34 - 37
Unit 10	Week 2	Page 347	Spin a Sum	Pages 38 - 41

Our Favorites

MATHEMATICS FOCUS

Representing Data

Organizing information makes it easier to discuss and interpret. Data can be presented using pictures and symbols.

Children make up three questions about favorites to ask the class. They draw pictures to answer the questions, sort the data, and present it on a poster.

....

MATERIALS

❑ chart paper

❑ eighth sheets of paper

❑ three legal-size envelopes

❑ 12" x 18" drawing paper

❑ scissors

❑ paste

PREPARATION Tape each legal-size envelope to an $8\frac{1}{2}$" x 11" sheet of paper. Before the second session, copy sets of the class's data.

TIME 4 sessions

WRITING FOCUS

Interpreting Favorites

Putting thoughts into drawing and writing and noting how a sentence begins and ends are two of the first steps to becoming writers.

Children interpret information on their posters, then write complete sentences to report their findings.

....

MATERIALS

❑ chart paper

❑ writing paper

TIME 1 session

Representing Data

Finding ways to organize our answers and report them is the big challenge.

ASKING QUESTIONS

1 *Let's see what we can find out about each other's favorite things.* Take a quick poll to find out the children's favorite colors. Write the results on the chalkboard. *What other "favorites" questions could we ask to learn more about each other?* Write on chart paper the children's suggestions, and read them aloud.

2 Choose three questions for the class to answer. Write each of the three questions on an envelope. Post the envelopes where everyone can reach them. *For each question, draw an answer and put your name on it. Put each drawing in the envelope for the question it answers.*

3 At the end of math time, tell the class that, starting tomorrow, they will look at everyone's answers and see what they can find out.

4 Before the next math time, arrange each envelope's answers on an 11″ × 17″ sheet of paper and photocopy the three sets for each pair.

LOOKING AT ANSWERS

5 Each day, meet at the rug. Spread out the answers from one envelope and talk about what the children notice.

- *Do you see the drawing you made?*

- *Do you see some that are like yours? that are different?*

- *What is a way we could sort these answers?* Sort the pictures according to several suggestions.

- *How many favorites are something sweet, like a dessert?* Ask other *How many?* questions.

6 At their seats, have pairs cut apart the photocopied answers for the day's questions, organize them on drawing paper, and paste them down. Help each pair write on their poster a sentence that begins: "We found out _____." Post the children's recordings on the wall.

Interpreting Favorites

Our walls are covered with posters! Now we write about what we learn from them.

GATHERING DATA FROM POSTERS

1 Focus the children's attention on the posters in general. Then spend some time talking about individual posters.

- *Who can tell us something about the favorites of our class by looking at these posters?*

- *How many different favorite things have we shown on our posters?*

- *On this poster, which (animal) did most of you choose?*

- *What are the different categories on this poster?*

REPORTING ON OUR OWN

Favorites

Lots of kids like pizza best.

Only one person likes turtles best of all.

Six different animals were said.

2 *Let's make a report about our favorites. What are some things we know about our favorites?* Write the children's responses on chart paper. Use the children's exact language, encouraging them to put their ideas into complete sentences.

3 As you write the children's sentences, informally talk about appropriate capitalization, punctuation, and spacing of words.

- *What does this mark at the end of the sentence mean?*

- *Why did I make this a big "L"?*

- *Why is there a space here and here in this sentence?*

4 *Now it's your turn to be writers.* Have the children write about something they learned about the class favorites.

> You will observe a wide variation in children's writing skills–drawings, strings of letters, individual words, complete thoughts, and a mixture of invented and conventional spelling. Some children may just copy the sentences written on the chart paper. Show your appreciation and enjoyment of all the children's writing.

BEGINNING THE REVISION PROCESS

5 When the children finish writing, focus their attention on their own papers. *Point to where you wrote your name on your writing.* Make sure all the children include their names.

> The simple step of checking that their names are on their papers helps children become acquainted with the revision stage of the writing process and promotes a sense of authorship.

SHARING OUR REPORTS

6 Provide time for the students to share their writing with the class. You may want to do this in short sessions throughout the day or over the next few days.

> It is important that the children's writing be honored—given a moment in the spotlight before the class, on a library shelf, or at home with family members. Make time in this first writing activity for all the children to share their writing with the class. As they share, you will also have the opportunity to model listening and responding skills.

ASSESSMENT

This first writing endeavor will let you evaluate where each child is in his understanding of the written language.

- *Did the child use words or pictures to communicate meaning?*
- *Did the child report his thinking?*

(Classroom Talk)

MODELING

Modeling is an effective teaching strategy. Writing and thinking aloud in front of the children allows them to construct for themselves the meaning and importance of writing. In addition, modeling allows the teacher the opportunity to experience the kind of thinking involved in the writing experience.

In this lesson, model making statements about the class's favorites expressed in complete sentences. As you write the children's own words on chart paper, model appropriate writing mechanics. Be sure to think aloud as you are writing.

- *I'll begin this sentence with a capital letter.*
- *'Turtle', that starts with 't'.*

Fences, Roads, and Walls

MATHEMATICS FOCUS

Creating Patterns

Patterns can be expressed in a variety of ways: physically, verbally, and with objects. The same pattern can be translated from one medium to another.

Children copy a motion pattern each day, then translate that pattern into other motions, sounds, and designs. Recordings of the pattern are made in several ways, compared, and discussed.

••

MATERIALS   For each pair

❑   100 LinkerCubes in mixed colors

❑   Pattern Blocks (9 of each shape)

❑   Pattern Block Stickers (24 of each shape)

PREPARATION   Put each pair's stickers in an envelope. Cut 11" x 17" sheets of paper into $5\frac{1}{2}$" x 17" strips, or 12" x 18" into 6" x 18".

TIME   4 sessions

WRITING FOCUS

Recording Patterns

Asking children to record their mathematics allows them to use words and pictures. Children reveal in drawings the tie between their understandings and the physical contexts of their learning.

Children discover a pattern in a story, then hunt for patterns in other places. They record what they find and share the recordings, looking for ways their patterns are alike.

••

MATERIALS

❑   pattern book, such as *Brown Bear, Brown Bear*, by Bill Martin, Jr.

❑   chart paper

❑   writing or drawing paper

❑   colored markers or crayons

PREPARATION   Plan the itinerary for a pattern hunt. Create a bulletin board to display the children's recordings.

TIME   2 sessions

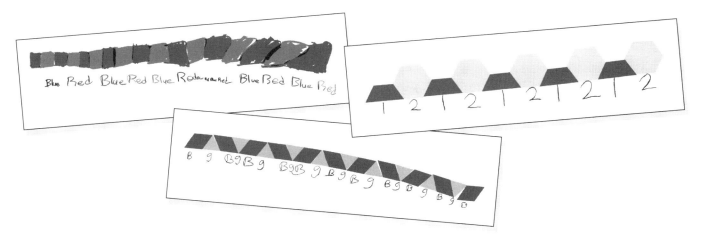

Allowing children to come up with their own ways of labeling patterns yields interesting results. Some children who write color words to start with may end up using the shorthand of just writing the initials or using numerals in subsequent recordings.

Creating Patterns

As we translate patterns into different forms, we understand that sequences can be alike because they have the same pattern.

TRANSLATING PATTERNS

1 Start out by introducing a motion pattern. Ask children to watch, listen, and join in as you make a pattern with your hands: snap, clap, snap, clap. ***What's another way to act out this same pattern?*** Try out the ways children offer, checking that the suggestions all follow the *abababab* pattern.

2 ***How could we record this pattern on the chalkboard?*** Record the pattern in the ways the children suggest. ***How could you make something with your LinkerCubes that will remind you of this pattern?*** As children finish modeling the pattern with cubes, have several of them show their models and tell about their thinking.

3 Repeat this activity as time permits. Choose from these pattern structures: *aabaabaab, abbabbabb, abcabcabc, aabbaabbaabb.*

RECORDING PATTERNS

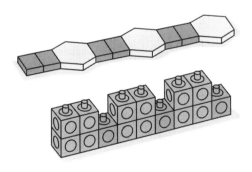

4 Each day, for the next several days, ask a child to perform a motion pattern for the class to copy. Translate it to another motion sequence, then talk about the ways you could record the pattern on the chalkboard. ***How could we use words? letters? other ways?***

5 Challenge the children to use the same pattern to make a wall or fence or road with LinkerCubes or Pattern Blocks.

6 When children are ready, have them record what they've made using stickers or crayons and words, letters, or numbers. Ask children who finish one recording to do another design with the same pattern.

7 When most children have finished, pass the recordings around the room for others to see. Return the recordings to their owners and discuss some of them. ***How is this pattern like the one we did at the start of math time?***

Recording Patterns

How can we make a record to share with others the patterns we find?

HUNTING FOR PATTERNS

I see the stripes on her sweater.

The cubbies go red, green, blue, red, green, blue.

1. Follow math time by reading a pattern book like *Brown Bear, Brown Bear* by Bill Martin, Jr. After the reading, talk about the pattern in the story.

2. ***There are patterns in math. There are patterns in stories. Where else might we find patterns?*** Challenge the children to look around and find patterns inside the classroom. Perhaps patterns can be found in floor tiles, rugs, clothing, and bulletin board displays.

3. Explain to the children that they will be going on a pattern hunt. Have pairs take paper and pencils to record the patterns they find.

   > Encourage conversation during the hunt; the observations of one child will inspire others to keep up the search. Call the attention of the group to interesting patterns the pairs discover.

WRITING ABOUT PATTERNS

I saw a pattern in the tiles in the hall.

And the bricks in the front of the school make a pattern.

4. After the hunt, have the children talk about the patterns they saw. Write their pattern discoveries on chart paper.

5. Invite the children to make a record of the patterns to share with others. Encourage them to draw a picture of a pattern they found on the hunt, then use words, letters, or numbers to tell about the patterns.

6. It may be helpful to write a prompt such as, "I found a pattern in _____." on the chalkboard. Ask volunteers to finish the sentence orally as a model for other children.

   > Sentence starters and writing formats throughout *Writing Mathematics* are presented as frames to support children as they develop independence as writers. Although a powerful modeling tool, formats should never constrain the children's own thinking or creativity. Show your appreciation of the unique ways of organizing writing children invent, and use their ideas as models.

CONFERENCING ABOUT REVISION

7 As the children work independently, conference briefly with individuals. Ask them to share their recording with you. Respond to something you genuinely enjoyed, then ask one or two questions that prompt the child to make the recording more clear or add new information.

8 Instead of telling the children how to revise, use questions that draw the need for revisions from the child. The following are some questions to ask in conferences.

- *Tell me about your picture. What could you write down about that?*

- *Can you tell me more?* As the child tells you more, say, *How can you add that to what you've written?*

> Because young children's thinking surpasses their ability to write, many will embellish what they have written as they "read" their writing to an interested audience. Encourage children to include the additional details in their recordings during the revision stage.

SHARING PATTERNS

9 Gather the children to share their pattern recordings. Talk about how the patterns they recorded are alike. Display the finished recordings on the bulletin board.

ASSESSMENT

To assess this writing activity, evaluate how well the children communicate their understanding of patterns in their recordings.

- *Did the child find patterns in the environment and record them?*

- *Did the child make a recording to share?*

(Classroom Talk)

THE WRITING CONFERENCE

Writing conferences should continue throughout the year, providing information about each child's progress and encouraging children to develop their skills. During conferences, keep the following points in mind.

- Encourage the child to read her writing to you.
- Show an interest in what the child has to say, both orally and in writing.
- Take note of the child's strengths and weaknesses in oral and written language.
- Sit beside the child and leave the pencil in the child's hand.
- Most importantly, be positive.

Toss and Make

MATHEMATICS FOCUS

Comparing Numbers

Any number can be represented with objects in many different ways. Numerals are a way to record *how many*. The ten frame is a tool for exploring how numbers relate to 10.

Children explore how numbers relate to 10 as they play a game, tossing a 0-9 die and showing the number with LinkerCubes on a ten frame. They make each new number rolled from the number they just made.

....

MATERIALS For each pair

❑ 20 LinkerCubes (10 each of two colors)

❑ 0-9 die

PREPARATION For each pair, make a copy of the Ten Frame (page 42). To prevent the dice from falling on the floor, you can put each die in a box with a clear lid (such as a stationery box) for shaking.

TIME 1 session

WRITING FOCUS

Reporting Experiences

Answering the questions *Who, What, When,* and *Where* is helpful for recalling and reporting experiences.

Children discuss newspapers and the *who, what, when,* and *where* of newspaper writing. Children write and illustrate articles about their math game and publish them in a bulletin board newspaper.

....

MATERIALS

❑ newspaper

❑ chart paper

❑ writing paper

PREPARATION Create a bulletin board for the class's news reports.

TIME 1 session

How to Play Toss and Make

- Partners need a ten frame, a 0-9 die, and 10 cubes each.
- In turn, each player throws the die and shows that many cubes on the ten frame, putting on cubes from his pile if the number is larger, or taking off cubes and adding them to his pile if the number is smaller. If the die shows 0, the player may add or take off any number 1 to 10.
- The game ends when a player runs out of cubes.
- For variation, the game could be played without the ten frame.

Comparing Numbers

Playing this game helps us see relationships between numbers.

LEARNING THE GAME

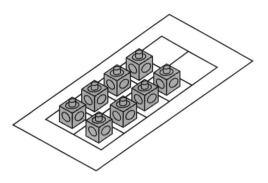

1 Distribute copies of the Ten Frame and dice to the pairs of children. ***Let's look at the game board for today's game. What do you notice about it?*** Children should see there are 5 spaces and 5 more spaces.

2 Throw a die and say the number. Have each pair show that number of cubes on their ten frame. Then roll the die again. ***Think of a way to make the new number on the ten frame.***

3 Toss the die several more times to get the children used to the idea of making the number on the die. Emphasize this by saying for example, ***Make 5***, for a roll of 5.

4 Introduce the children to the rules of the game, and have them play in pairs.

PLAYING THE GAME

I rolled 2, so I just took off all the cubes except these 2.

I tossed 9, so I just filled up all the spaces except one.

5 While the children play the game, observe one pair at a time, asking them to explain their thinking when they make a move.

> You'll notice a wide variety of strategies. Some children will feel they need to take all the cubes off the ten frame in order to make a new number, others will count on or back from the number that is there. For example, if 4 cubes are already on the frame, they know they can add 2 more to make 6 or remove 1 to make 3. You may notice that children's strategies change as they play the game.

6 At the end of math time, discuss the game.

- *How could you tell when to put more cubes on the ten frame or take some off?*

- *How does the ten frame help you know how many cubes there are?*

- *How could you know, without counting from 1, if 10 are on the ten frame? What about 9? 8?*

Reporting Experiences

We become the publishers and writers of a new math newspaper.

RECALLING AN EXPERIENCE

We rolled a lot of numbers before there was a winner.

1 Show the children a newspaper. Talk about its purpose–to tell about what is going on in our city, state, country, and world. Informally use and discuss newspaper vocabulary such as *article, headline,* and *by-line.*

2 Explain to the children that they are going to write newspaper reports to tell about what they did in math. *Newspaper writers always tell what, who, when, and where.* Pose the "4 W" questions to the children and accept several responses to each question.

- *What did we do in math today?*
- *Who did you play the game with?*
- *When did you play the game?*
- *Where did you play the game?*

RECORDING OUR EXPERIENCE

3 Have the children draw a picture and write about the math game. *Be sure your picture and writing tell what you played, who you played with, when you played, and where you played.*

The Room Nine Times

Is It Luck? Nancy	Make a Number Jason	Playing and Learning Alex	A New Game Ramona	A Winner Everytime Candy	Great strategies Daniel
Meet Toss and Make Kevin	You Can Play Rachel	No More cubes! Tomio	The Winner is Shani	Get Ready, Get Set, Toss Marcus	Roll and Make Alexis

REVISING OUR NEWS REPORTS

4 After the children are finished writing their news articles, ask them to reread them and think of a headline. *Write the headline for your article at the top of your paper. Be sure you include your by-line* (name) *as well.*

EXTRA! EXTRA!

5 Set aside some bulletin board space for children to post their math news articles. Encourage the children to add to the board independently throughout the year with interesting discoveries they are making in mathematics.

ASSESSMENT

To assess this writing activity, evaluate how well the children communicate the who, what, when, and where of the math activity in their news reports.

- *Did the child recall the important aspects of the math activity?*
- *Did the child include information about who, what, when, and where?*

(Classroom Talk)

CREATING AN ENVIRONMENT FOR DISCUSSIONS

Providing many opportunities for children to discuss their ideas is vital to their success in writing and mathematics. For discussions to be effective, the classroom must be a place where everyone's ideas are respected. Children need the freedom to think out loud–forming, evaluating, and revising their thoughts in the moment. What the children have come to think of as 'mistakes' they can learn to view as welcome, useful steps toward solutions and understandings.

Provide opportunities throughout the day for children to tell what happened, especially as they encounter new ideas. As the children talk about their experiences, bring other children into the dialog.

- *How is that like what you did? How is it different?*
- *Were your game results the same? Explain.*

How Many Outfits?

MATHEMATICS FOCUS

Drawing Possible Ways

Making an organized recording is helpful in finding all the solutions for a problem. When working on combinations problems, recognizing when a new way is different is the children's first step.

Children define what an outfit is and look over some jeans and shirts in preparation for finding out how many outfits they can make. Pairs draw pictures of outfits they find. The class's outfits are organized, and discussed.

⋯⋯⋯⋯⋯⋯⋯⋯⋯⋯⋯⋯⋯⋯⋯⋯

MATERIALS

❑ chart paper

❑ full sheets of paper

❑ colored markers or crayons

❑ a large piece of butcher paper for mounting the cut-out outfits.

TIME 2 sessions

WRITING FOCUS

Convincing Each Other

Sharing findings with others and writing to explain a solution are useful ways to prepare to discuss a problem.

Children compare the outfits they drew in the math activity. Pairs write, explaining their solution to another outfits problem, revise with partners, and try to convince others their solutions are correct.

⋯⋯⋯⋯⋯⋯⋯⋯⋯⋯⋯⋯⋯⋯⋯⋯

MATERIALS

❑ full sheets of paper

❑ writing paper

PREPARATION Pairs will need the recordings of outfits they made during the math activity.

TIME 1-2 sessions

Drawing Possible Ways

It's time to get dressed, and here's what we have to choose from: two pairs of jeans and three shirts.

DRAWING DIFFERENT OUTFITS

1 *Suppose you have two pairs of jeans. What colors might they be? What if you have three shirts? What colors could they be?* On the chart paper show two jeans colors and three shirt colors the children suggest and the question: *How many outfits? Is blue jeans and red shirt one possible outfit?*

2 *How many different outfits can you make?* Have each pair of children draw pictures to show the different outfits they find.

> Do not expect children to find all six solutions to this problem or to even approach the search in an organized way. Look for evidence that they recognize when a way is different and should be recorded.

LOOKING AT ALL OUR OUTFITS

3 Place a large piece of butcher paper on the rug. Have the children cut out each outfit from their recordings and group all the like outfits together on the paper. Discuss what children notice about the butcher paper recording.

- *What do you see?*
- *What are some ways we found?*
- *How many different ways did we find?*
- *How many of you made (white) jeans and (blue) shirts?*

4 Let some of the children paste the groups of outfits on the butcher paper. Other children can write things they notice about the class's work on the problem.

Convincing Each Other

We use our understanding of finding combinations to solve a new problem and explain how we did it.

COMPARING FINDINGS

1 After pairs have finished their pictures of different outfits, have them get together with another pair to compare what they've drawn. *Share the outfits you drew with another pair and compare them.*

2 Gather the class and talk about their findings.

- *What did you find out when you shared your outfits?*
- *Did you have outfits that were the same? different?*
- *Did you think of new outfits when you were sharing?*
- *How many different outfits did you find?*

EXPLAINING OUR THINKING

3 *You know a lot about the outfits. Here's a new problem: Do you have enough outfits to wear a different outfit to school each day for a week?* Take a moment to check that children understand the problem.

Yes, there are enough outfits. We think this because _____.

No, there are not enough outfits. We think this because _____.

4 Tell the children they should use words and drawings to tell what they figure out. On chart paper, print the two frame sentences shown and read them with the class. Explain that when the pairs have solved the problem, they can use the frame that fits their solution to write their explanation. Have the children work on this problem with the partners they had in the math activity.

> As in the math activity, for this problem it is not essential that children know there are enough outfits. What is important is that they are able to tell about their thinking in their explanations.

EDITING WITH PARTNERS

5 When pairs have finished their explanations, ask a volunteer to read hers to you while the class observes. Sit beside the child and model the role of editing partner. Listen carefully. Praise the writer's efforts and ask one or two questions to help the child make her writing more clear.

6 Match up children to be editing partners. The pairs should take turns, one child reading while the other child listens and responds. Provide time for the children to make revisions.

CONVINCE ME!

7 When all the pairs are satisfied with their explanations, bring the class together. Follow the guidelines for "Convince Me!" discussions below as you facilitate discussion of the children's solutions.

ASSESSMENT

To assess this joint writing effort, listen to and observe each child's participation in the pair's construction of an explanation.

- *Did the child contribute to the thinking and to the pair's way of presenting their explanation?*
- *Did the child note like and different outfits?*

(Classroom Talk)

"CONVINCE ME!" DISCUSSIONS

As children work out solutions using their own approaches, they develop confidence and critical-thinking skills. Find opportunities to pose problems for discussion as a regular part of your curriculum. Here are some guidelines for "Convince Me!" discussions.

- After presenting a problem, allow time for children to think about how to solve it. Ask several children to respond. Record the different solutions on the chalkboard.
- Do not indicate the rightness or wrongness of different answers. Be aware of hints your body language or the inflection of your voice might convey.
- Encourage debate about the correct solution, requesting that children "convince" you and each other of their thinking.
- Ask for several different explanations for the problem in question. *Does everyone agree? Can someone tell us a different way to think about it?*

Upstairs, Downstairs

MATHEMATICS FOCUS

Inventing Number Stories

Number pairs can be used to describe another number. If the number of a group of objects is known and some are hidden, the number of objects remaining can be used to determine how many are hidden.

The class makes a set of peek-a-boo houses for 5 mice. Children then make peek-a-boo houses to show combinations for numbers 5 to 10, record the numbers for wholes and parts, and tell the hidden numbers.

· ·

MATERIALS

- ❏ chart paper
- ❏ full sheets of paper
- ❏ scissors
- ❏ colored markers or crayons

PREPARATION   Cut 6 peek-a-boo houses out of construction paper.

TIME   4-5 sessions

WRITING FOCUS

Reporting About Numbers

Writing about one of the numbers 5 to 10 provides an opportunity for children to consolidate their learning about number combinations and to communicate what they know.

The class discusses the number combinations for several numbers. Each child then writes "all about" one number from 5 to 10, and these descriptions are bound into class books.

· ·

MATERIALS

- ❏ chart paper
- ❏ writing paper

PREPARATION   Provide supplies for covering and binding class books.

TIME   2 sessions

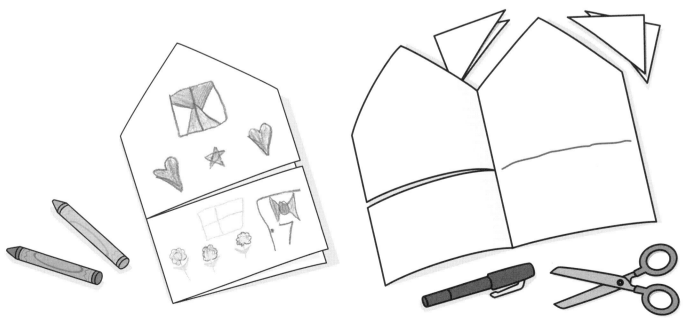

Inventing Number Stories

Creating number stories is fun because each story goes in a peek-a-boo book.

TELLING ONE WAY

1 Show a house. Explain that it is a mouse house. *Who can tell me one way a family of 5 mice could be in the house? I want to know how many are upstairs and how many are downstairs.*

2 Draw the mice in the house the way a child suggests. Ask what numbers tell how many are upstairs and downstairs and write them as shown. On the cover page, write the number in all–5.

3 *Who can think of another way for the 5 mice to be in the house?* Draw the mice in a new house the way a child suggests and write the numbers. Continue this way until you show all the ways 5 mice can be in the house. Then, as you open up one house at a time, have the children tell, in unison: how many mice in all, how many upstairs, and how many downstairs *(5 is 3 and 2)*.

4 Cover the downstairs of a house and tell how many again *(5 is 3 and...)* but this time let children guess how many are hidden. Open the downstairs and say the whole sentence *(5 is 3 and 2)*. Do this for all the houses, then start over, this time covering the upstairs.

CREATING OUR OWN STORIES

At dinosaur house, 6 is 4 upstairs and 2 downstairs.

5 *You are each going to make your own house stories, about anything you like.* Have the class brainstorm ideas for story characters and record the ideas on chart paper. Show the children how to make the houses.

6 Each day, have children choose a different character and number from 5 to 10, then make as many stories as time allows. Provide time for children to share their stories with partners.

Reporting About Numbers

We're ready to write the book. We have become very familiar with the numbers 5 through 10 and their parts.

TELLING ABOUT NUMBERS

1 *We've done a lot of thinking about numbers and number combinations. Tell me what you know about the number 7 and the number combinations that make 7.* Encourage discussion about several numbers and their combinations. Write children's responses on chart paper. *Can you tell a story about that number combination?*

> To develop a writing climate in your classroom, write daily in front of the children. Sit close to the children and write slowly on large chart paper. Think aloud as you write. Involve the children, asking for opinions and seeking advice about spelling, word choice, or punctuation.

WRITING ABOUT NUMBERS

2 Challenge the children to choose a number from 5 to 10 and record everything they know about the number. *Use words, pictures, and numbers to tell about the number you choose.* Tell the children that their descriptions "all about" numbers will go into class books.

> Posing an open-ended writing task allows the children to approach the challenge at their own levels. You will have the opportunity to observe children's preference for using drawings or writing; their interest and perseverance in telling all they know; and, possibly, their willingness to investigate more complex number combinations without prompting, for example, 7 is 2 and 2 and 2 and 1.

3 As the children work side by side, encourage them to share their ideas for writing. This access to each other's approaches enriches the environment in which the children write, providing many models and teaching the value of collaboration.

REVISING WITH PARTNERS

4 Before the children share their writing with the class, have them share it with a partner. Talk with the children about ways they can listen and respond to their partner's writing. Write the children's suggestions on chart paper.

- *What are some things we can do while we listen to our partner read?*

- *What are some things we can do after the reading to help our partners think about their writing?*

OUR "ALL ABOUT" BOOKS

5 You may want to have all the children who wrote about the number 5 share their writing at one time, and continue in this way over several more sharing times.

6 Bind the children's writing into number books. Have one book titled, *All About 5* and other books with similar titles for the other numbers explored. Arrange to have these stories shared with others outside of the class.

ASSESSMENT

To assess this writing activity, evaluate how well the children communicate their understanding of number pairs in "all about" reports.

- *Did the child use the "all about" format to consolidate her learning?*

- *Did the child use the "all about" format to communicate what she knows?*

───────(Classroom Talk)───────

THE TEACHER'S ROLE IN DISCUSSIONS

As a facilitator of discussions about thinking and ideas, the teacher's role changes from the traditional one of asking questions for which she already knows the answers, waiting for responses, and imposing the 'right/wrong' judgment, to the challenge of posing open-ended questions, extending students' thinking, and orchestrating the exchange of ideas between children.

As children share their peek-a-boo houses, challenge others to become involved and encourage children to debate their differing viewpoints.

- *Nick, do you agree that there are three dinosaurs downstairs? Why or why not?*
- *Lydia tells us there are 10 cats in her house. Before she shares her story, what are some possible ways the cats might be in the house? Does everyone agree? Does anyone have another way the cats might be in the house? Lydia, did anyone say how the cats are in your house? Tell us your story.*
- *Did anyone make a house that is similar to this house in some way? Tell us about your house and how it is similar.*

Teddy and Me

MATHEMATICS FOCUS

Comparing Attributes

A special kind of sorting situation calls for sorting a group of objects using comparison with one object as a referent.

Children bring stuffed animals from home and compare them, using such words as *bigger, taller, shorter*. They make portraits of their animals, being sure to include distinguishing attributes.

....

MATERIALS

❑ 12" x 18" drawing paper (or larger to trace outlines of large stuffed animals)

❑ scissors

❑ colored markers or crayons

PREPARATION   It's a good idea to have a few "extra" stuffed animals, for those who don't bring one from home.

TIME   1 session

WRITING FOCUS

Describing Our Animals

Information can be gathered through observation. Descriptive words are useful for writing to describe the stuffed animals.

Children describe stuffed animals, talking about and using descriptive words. The children then write descriptions of their animals and revise them in preparation for playing a guessing game.

....

MATERIALS

❑ chart paper

❑ writing paper

TIME   1-2 sessions

Comparing Attributes

We admire our wonderful collection of stuffed animals. How many different types there are!

MAKING COMPARISONS

Robbie's animal is taller, but mine has a bigger tummy.

1 Bring all the children and their stuffed animals to the rug. Go around the circle, having the children introduce their animals.

2 *Let's do some comparing.* Call on a child to put his animal in the center. ***Do any of you think your animal is taller than this?*** Let volunteers bring their animals to the center of the rug to compare. Put taller animals in one group, shorter animals in another group, and animals the same height in a third group.

3 Let the children make three-group comparisons of the animals' characteristics. Let the particular make-up of the class's animal collection suggest the types of comparisons. Some possible suggestions are:

- animal type
- bigger or smaller ears
- lighter or darker color
- more or less fuzzy
- younger or older
- bigger or smaller feet
- bigger or smaller tummy

DRAWING PORTRAITS

4 Show the children how to trace outlines of their animals on paper which they can color to make life-size portraits. Display these along your walls.

Describing Our Animals

There are a lot of ways to describe all the different types of animals we have!

TALKING TO DESCRIBE

1 Set up 5 or 6 stuffed animals where the children can see them. *I'll describe one of these animals and you try to guess which one it is.* Model descriptive language such as, *It is not the smallest animal* and *It is black and white.* Keep giving clues until every child knows which animal you are describing. Repeat the process with other animals.

2 Ask for volunteers to take over your role as describer. Talk about descriptive words and the kinds of clues that make it easier to choose the correct animal. Also discuss clues that make the guessing too easy, such as saying the animal's name or something that clearly describes only one animal.

> You will want to have the children pay attention to the kinds of words they are using to describe the different characteristics of their animals. Their language will be imprecise at first, as they confuse taller with bigger, for example, but will improve over time.

WRITING TO DESCRIBE

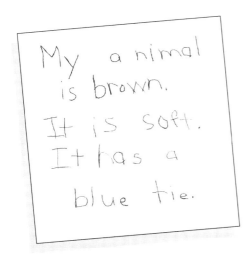

My animal is brown. It is soft. It has a blue tie.

3 *Now, write a description of your own stuffed animal.* Tell the children that later their descriptions will be read aloud. The class will try to identify the animal that is described. *Remember not to include your animal's name.*

4 As the children enjoy the mystery of writing to an anticipated audience, encourage them to think about the listeners' reactions and responses.

- *Will your classmates know enough to identify the animal you are describing?*

- *Is there more than one animal that fits your description?*

REVISING FOR COMPLETENESS

5 A word bank of comparison words may help children as they revise their writing. Have children suggest the words to include. While children are revising, visit individuals and talk about the descriptive words they are using.

- *Will you show me where you've written one of the words on our chart?*
- *Is there another word on the chart that you could use in your description?*

WHICH ANIMAL IS IT?

6 Once the children's descriptions have been revised, collect them. Read the descriptions out loud, one at a time, and have the class guess which animal is being described. Encourage debate if different animals are identified for the same description.

- *Are these two animals different?*
- *What clue could be given that would tell you it's this one?*
- *Is there something about this animal that is different from all the rest?*

ASSESSMENT

Use the class's responses to the descriptions to help you evaluate how well the children communicate their understanding of sorting in their descriptions.

- *Did the child use descriptive language to write about her animal?*
- *Did the child's description for the guessing game challenge the class?*

(Classroom Talk)

DEVELOPING MATHEMATICAL VOCABULARY

Throughout mathematics, specialized vocabulary is necessary for concise and effective communication. In this activity children use the language of comparison and descriptive words to sort and tell about their stuffed animals. To promote vocabulary development, keep the following suggestions in mind.

- Introduce and use all mathematical vocabulary as tools for talking about ideas.
- Show appreciation for children's efforts to use new words and symbols. Address errors in usage informally as children work and talk.
- Challenge children to listen as words and symbols are used during activities, then have students discuss their meanings. If you write definitions on the board, use the children's language as much as possible.

Bears on the Bus

MATHEMATICS FOCUS

Creating Addition Stories

Equations are one way to summarize a story about objects. All parts of an equation have meaning, not just the answer.

Children learn to use equations. Partners act out addition stories on workmats, write an equation to summarize each story, and put the equations on an addition chart.

MATERIALS For each pair

❑ 18 Teddy Bear Counters in two colors (9 of each color)
❑ 10 Pattern Block squares
❑ full sheets of paper
❑ eighth sheets of paper

PREPARATION Write the three bear stories on chart paper. Prepare a bulletin board as shown below.

TIME 4 sessions

WRITING FOCUS

Reporting Experiences

Story frames provide a format for communicating in writing stories that have been told orally and represented using equations.

Children tell some of the stories they've invented, then write one story to act out on a favorite workmat. These are published in a class book that students can take home.

MATERIALS

❑ writing paper (the same size as the paper used for workmats)

PREPARATION Leave the three bear story frames on display. Provide supplies for covering and binding class books.

TIME 2 sessions

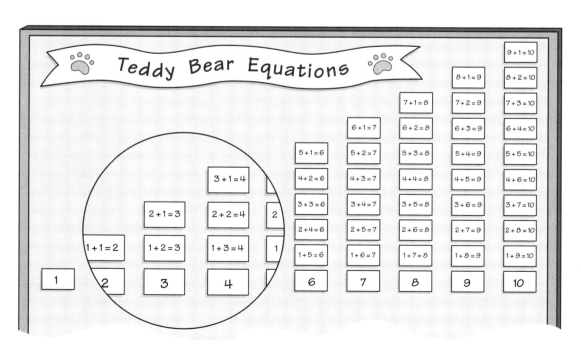

Creating Addition Stories

It's fun to see how many different addition equations we can generate through our teddy bear stories.

ACTING OUT EQUATIONS

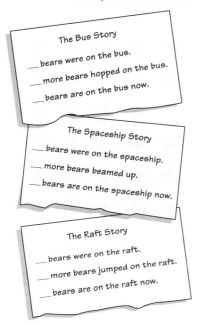

The Bus Story
___bears were on the bus.
___more bears hopped on the bus.
___bears are on the bus now.

The Spaceship Story
___bears were on the spaceship.
___more bears beamed up.
___bears are on the spaceship now.

The Raft Story
___bears were on the raft.
___more bears jumped on the raft.
___bears are on the raft now.

WRITING EQUATIONS

6 + 2 = 8

1 Display the three teddy bear stories and read each one with the children. Explain that the blanks are there so the story can be told many times, each time with different numbers of bears.

2 *Let's act out a bus story together.* Arrange 10 chairs in two rows of 5. Help children act out the story. *Three bears were on the bus. 2 more bears hopped on the bus. 5 bears are on the bus now.*

3 *I'm going to show you a special way to write what we just said.* On the chalkboard, write the equation: 3 + 2 = 5. Point as you read: *3 plus 2 equals 5; 3 bears on the bus, 2 more get on, 5 all together; 3 and 2 is 5. This way of writing about what happened is called an* equation.

4 Act out other stories, using the three stories as frames. After each story, have the children help you write the equation.

5 *Now it's your turn to make up stories and write equations.* Each day, have partners choose a different story setting and create a workmat. On the workmat they should put 10 Pattern Block squares to form seats.

6 *Make up stories and act them out with Teddy Bear Counters on your workmat.* Explain that one child should put teddy bears in one color on some of the seats, and the partner put bears in another color on other seats. On an eighth sheet of paper they write an equation to tell what happened.

7 *When you finish an equation, tack it on the chart above the number of bears in all and start a new story with a different number of bears.* An equation already on the chart can be tacked over earlier equations.

8 Near the end of math time, have pairs use their workmats to act out for the class equations from the chart.

Reporting Experiences

Which of our stories do we want to write up and put in the class book?

RECALLING ADDITION STORIES

1 Give the children time to tell some of the stories they've created, acting them out on their workmats. Encourage them to think about how the stories and equations are similar to the ones they created on previous days.

- *Tell me your teddy bear story. What equation tells about your story?*

- *Did anyone else create a story mat that is like this one?*

- *Which of your workmats and stories is your favorite?*

WRITING ADDITION STORIES

2 *You've told many stories over the last few days. Let's create a class book of some of your stories.* Have the children choose a favorite workmat and write an addition story and the equation. The workmat, story, and equation will go into the book. Review the story frames that were used in the math activity, and keep them posted for children to refer to as they write.

3 As the children are working on their stories, circulate around the room and ask children who are having difficulty starting to share their stories with you. Verbalizing first may help children put a story into writing.

EDITING FOR CORRECTNESS

4 Have the children exchange mats and stories with a partner. *Read your partner's story and act it out on the workmat.*

- *Does the story make sense?*

- *Do you agree with the equation?*

OUR ADDITION STORY BOOK

5 When the addition stories are finished, talk with the children about the order in which to put the pages for the class book. Bind the book so each story is on the left page and its workmat on the right. This way, readers can read a story and work the addition at the same time.

6 The completed book will no doubt be a class favorite. Read the stories to the children during story time and allow the children to take the book home for a night to share with their families. You may want to send home a bag of Teddy Bear Counters, too.

ASSESSMENT

To assess this writing activity, evaluate how well the children communicate their understanding of addition in their teddy bear stories and equations.

- *Did the child write a story about what she acted out on her workmat?*

- *Did the child use one of the three bear stories or create an original one?*

(Classroom Talk)

ORAL LANGUAGE AND WRITING

Oral language is the foundation of writing. The discussions which take place prior to writing focus children's thinking about the writing task, draw upon their prior knowledge, build vocabulary, and begin a conversation about new concepts. The goal is that all children leave discussions with confidence they have something to say.

Oral language experiences prior to writing can take many different forms, including brainstorming, role playing, sharing literature, holding large and small group discussions, and interviewing peers.

During the writing activity, observe the children as they write. At this age, the very act of forming letters can be a challenge, limiting the extent to which children's writing mimics their oral language. If a child is struggling, not with the act of writing, but with what to write, ask the child to tell you about what he is doing or thinking. Once the child has articulated a thought, ask the child to write that idea on paper.

Number Switch

MATHEMATICS FOCUS

Exploring A Sequence

There is a system to the way numbers are written. A mental picture of the Hundred Number Board is a powerful tool for mental arithmetic.

Children play two games on the Hundred Number Board, discuss their experiences, and make up their own games, to play during free time.

....

PREPARATION For each pair, make two copies on card stock of the Hundred Number Board Sections (pages 43-46). On one copy, cut the squares apart to make the tiles. On the other copy, cut the borders off so children can tape the four sections to make their boards.

TIME 2 sessions

WRITING FOCUS

Explaining How We Know

Being able to think about thinking and to communicate about it are important aspects of doing and writing mathematics.

Children put a group of numbers in numerical order and explain orally how they know theirs is a correct sequence. They do the same in letters to their families.

....

MATERIALS

❑ writing paper

PREPARATION Make a copy of the Dear Family letter (page 47) for each child.

TIME 1-2 sessions

How to Play Hidden Numbers

- Partners put Number Tiles 1 to 100 in the correct places on the Hundred Number Board.

- One player hides his eyes, as the other turns over one of the tiles to hide a number.

- The first player looks and tries to name the hidden number.

- The players turn the tile over to check the number.

- Players take turns hiding eyes and hiding numbers.

How to Play Number Switch

- Partners put Number Tiles 1 to 100 in the correct places on the Hundred Number Board.

- While one player hides his eyes, the other switches two tiles in the same row.

- The first player looks and tries to find the two Number Tiles that were switched.

- When the switched tiles are found, the players return the tiles back to the correct places.

- Players take turns hiding eyes and switching numbers.

Exploring A Sequence

We use the way the numbers are arranged on the board to help us name hidden numbers and detect switched tiles.

PLAYING HIDDEN NUMBERS

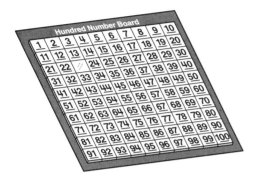

1 Distribute the four sections of the Hundred Number Board to each pair. Have the pairs arrange the four boards so the numbers read from 1 to 100. Let a volunteer explain the proper arrangement while you diagram it on the chalkboard. Then have pairs tape their sections together. Distribute the sets of cut apart number tiles to pairs.

2 Explain the game, *Hidden Numbers*, to the class. Encourage pairs to play it several times.

3 After the children have played a while, encourage them to tell about their thinking by having several pairs demonstrate the game and letting the child who names the hidden number tell *how she knows*.

4 Vary the game by telling the children to hide not just one, but several, numbers at a time. They could try hiding three or four numbers in a row or all the numbers in a square area.

> Some pairs may spend so much time setting up the board that they don't get to play the game. Don't worry if this happens—they are probably working on the part of the activity that is the most important to their learning.

PLAYING NUMBER SWITCH

Pick 5 tiles, and try to put them in the right places on a blank Hundred Number Board.

5 Explain the game, *Number Switch*, to the class. Have pairs play it several times.

6 For variations of *Number Switch*, have the children switch any two tiles on the board. After the children have played for a while, ask, **Which switches are most difficult to find?**

7 Offer pairs the choice of continuing to play *Number Switch* or of making up their own game on the Hundred Number Board.

8 Invite pairs to share with the class any games they invented. Encourage the class to play these games during free time.

Explaining How We Know

We think about how we know the order in which numbers go. Can we explain how we know in a letter to our families?

LOOKING FOR NUMBER SWITCHES

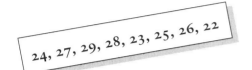

24, 27, 29, 28, 23, 25, 26, 22

1 Write a series of numbers out of order on the chalkboard. *With your partner, write these numbers in their proper order.*

2 As partners work, walk around the room and make a note of the different sequences. Write them on the board, without indicating whether they are right or wrong. Encourage the children to convince each other of the correct number sequence and to identify the incorrect sequences. (See "Convince Me!" Discussions, Classroom Talk, page 17.)

- *Are these all correct ways to organize the numbers? Tell us why you think so.*

- *Does everyone agree? Please tell me what you're thinking.*

3 Provide the opportunity for everyone to share their thinking. As children recognize incorrect sequences and everyone agrees, erase these responses from the board. Continue with other mixed-up number sequences, such as: 53, 43, 23, 63, 33, 13, 73.

WRITING TO EXPLAIN

Letter Writing Format

Today's Date

Dear _____,

Body of the Letter

Love,

Your Name

4 *There's just no fooling you when it comes to putting numbers in their correct order. How do you figure out what order numbers go in?* Write the children's responses on chart paper.

5 On the chalkboard, write the mixed-up sequence 43, 37, 39, 47, 35, 41, 45. *Here is a group of numbers that are out of order. Put the numbers in order, then write a letter to someone in your family explaining how you knew the correct order of the numbers.* Demonstrate and discuss proper letter writing form.

Numbers just keep going 1, 2, 3, 4, 5, 6, 7, 8, 9, 10. Then they go with the 10s, 20s, 30s, on and on.

REVISING OUR WRITING

6 Have the children reread their letters to themselves. *Ask yourself,*

- *Is this my best writing?*

- *Do I have any more to say?*

- *Will the person that I'm writing to understand what I'm saying in my letter?*

- *What can I do to make my explanation better?*

LET ME EXPLAIN

Dear Family,

This week in math we've been exploring the numbers 1 to 100. To extend this learning experience, the children have written a letter to explain to you how they sequence a list of numbers. Please take the time to read their letter and write back to them. Send your response back to school with your child to share with the rest of the class.

Thank you,

_____

7 Send the letters home with the children. Attach a copy of the Dear Family cover letter to encourage a family member to respond.

8 Provide time for children to share the responses from their families. Talk about which parts of their explanations helped the families understand the children's thinking.

ASSESSMENT

Use the families' responses to help you evaluate how well the children communicate their understanding of the number sequence in their letters of explanation.

- *Did the child explain how she knew the order of the numbers?*

- *Did the child use the proper letter writing format?*

(Classroom Talk)

USING DISCOURSE TO PROMOTE THINKING

Children's thinking is revealed as they verbalize ideas. As children hear themselves and their peers articulate ideas, they begin to engage in processes of metacognition–monitoring, regulating, and evaluating. Participation in groups and in whole class discussions helps children generate new ideas and transfer what is learned to new situations with greater success.

I Spy a Shape

MATHEMATICS FOCUS

Classifying Shapes

Two-dimensional shapes can be classified by an important attribute–the number of sides. Squares and rectangles are not the only four-sided shapes.

Children play the game *I Spy*, looking for shapes that fit clues some of which tell the number of sides. They draw pictures of shapes, then start collections of shapes with three sides and shapes with four sides.

....

MATERIALS
❑ quarter sheets of paper

TIME 1 session

WRITING FOCUS

Reporting What We Know

A class-made book is an introduction to report writing. Choosing a fact to report on and reading the class's collection of shape facts foster an intuitive understanding of organizing, an important writing skill.

Children go on a hunt for shapes, then brainstorm a list of facts they know about shapes. Each child writes and illustrates one fact and edits their writing for publication in *Our Book About Shapes*.

....

MATERIALS
❑ full sheets of paper
❑ chart paper

PREPARATION Have ready materials to cover and bind the class book.

TIME 2 sessions

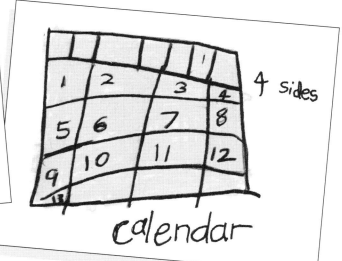

Classifying Shapes

We play a game that makes us focus on the shapes around us and the number of sides they have.

PLAYING I SPY

> I spy a shape with four sides. You open it to come into the classroom.

1 *Let's play a game of* I Spy. *Today we'll look for shapes. The special clue each time will be the number of sides the shape has.* Begin by modeling appropriate clues for the children. *I spy a shape with four sides. You can look through it to see outside.*

2 Have the child who guesses correctly go to the shape. *Can you count the number of sides the shape has?*

3 Let children take turns giving clues about a shape in the classroom. The first clue should always be the number of sides the shape has. Each time, have the guesser touch the sides of the shape as he counts them.

DRAWING SHAPES AROUND US

> The chalkboard has one, two, three, four sides. Two short and two long.

4 After the game has been played several times, tell the children that the class is going to start collections of shapes that have three sides and shapes that have four sides. *Did any of the shapes we spied in this room have three or four sides?*

5 On quarter sheets of paper, have the children draw pictures of shapes in the room that have three or four sides. On each drawing, have them write the name of the object and the number of sides.

> One, two, three, four sides!

Reporting What We Know

We become the authors of a book about shapes.

HUNTING FOR SHAPES

1 Take the class on a walk outside or around the school to look for three-and four-sided shapes. Children should bring along paper and pencils to sketch the shapes they find for their shapes collections.

2 Back in the classroom, have a discussion about their shapes. Record the children's findings on chart paper.

- *What are some things you noticed about the shapes you found?*

- *Which did you find more of–shapes with three sides or shapes with four sides? Why do you think that is so?*

WRITING ABOUT SHAPES

3 Explain to the children that, together, they will be creating a big book about shapes. *What are some things we will want to tell others about shapes?* As a class brainstorm a list of facts about shapes. Write the children's responses on chart paper.

4 Challenge the children to write and draw about one fact they know about shapes. Encourage children to do their drawing on a separate paper, so they can revise their writing later without disturbing their illustrations.

EDITING FOR PUBLICATION

5 Talk about the importance of editing writing others will read. Have children read their writing and look to see if their sentences begin with capital letters and end with periods. *Since we are going to be publishing this writing, let's pay particular attention to the spelling of our words.*

6 *Now it's time to make a final draft of your writing, with any changes you've decided to make.* Circulate as children write, helping those who need to get started or to stay focused. Show your appreciation for the effort children are investing in these final copies. Your attention will encourage the children to do their best.

OUR BOOK ABOUT SHAPES

7 When the children's final drafts are ready, bind the pages together to make a book about shapes, and choose one or two cover artists. Share the finished book with the class.

ASSESSMENT

To assess this writing activity, evaluate how well the children communicate their understanding of shapes in their page for the class book.

- *Did the child draw and write one fact about shapes?*

- *Did the child's illustration show creativity and understanding?*

─────(Classroom Talk)─────

WHAT ABOUT SPELLING?

The goal of *Writing Mathematics* is that children develop their ability to communicate in writing. When too much emphasis is placed on correct spelling, young children often limit the words they choose to use in order to avoid making spelling errors. This is probably the strongest reason to limit correction of spelling to the editing stage of the writing process. The following are suggested approaches.

- Encourage children not to worry about spelling in the pre-writing and writing stages. Assure children by demonstrating that you can read their writing as it is.

- Help parents understand that children are applying what they know about phonetic rules and that the children's own spelling is a very useful diagnostic tool for you.

- Let the emphasis on correct spelling depend on the purpose of each writing piece. Will these stories be published? Is this a journal entry that will be read only by the teacher?

- Use several strategies to help children edit for correct spelling, including developing word banks with the class, having children keep their own spelling dictionaries, holding individual writing conferences, and asking parents to volunteer during editing time.

Spin a Sum

MATHEMATICS FOCUS

Investigating Probability

Concepts of chance can be explored by organizing, recording, and describing outcomes of games that involve spinners. It is possible to determine what is likely under certain circumstances.

Children play the game *Spin a Sum* with partners and discuss the game. The game involves guessing, but the children find they can improve their luck by thinking before they guess.

....

MATERIALS   For each pair

❑   2 Transparent Spinners

❑   half sheets of paper

TIME   1 session

WRITING FOCUS

Giving Directions

Giving directions for playing a game inspires an exploration into what information directions include and how information is presented.

Children discuss what they know about directions and what they notice about commercial directions they examine. Children then write directions for playing *Spin a Sum* so they can play the game at home.

....

MATERIALS

❑   full sheets of paper

❑   chart paper

PREPARATION   Collect directions for games, recipes, craft projects, and other uses.

TIME   1-2 sessions

How to Play Spin a Sum

- Each player needs a four-part spinner labeled with numbers from 1 to 9. Each pair needs a half sheet of paper for recording.
- Each player selects a sum that can be made by adding a number from one of the spinners to a number from the other.
- Players spin their spinners at the same time, keeping track of the sums obtained by adding the two numbers indicated by the two spinners.
- The player whose sum is the first to come up twice wins.

Investigating Probability

We find we can consider the possible outcomes and make educated guesses about whose sum will be the first to come up twice.

MAKING OUR SPINNERS

1 *Let's learn a new game with number spinners. First, each of you needs to make a spinner.*

2 Show the children how to trace around a Transparent Spinner onto paper. Then have the children use their outlines to make their own spinners. *Inside the outlined space you traced, make four equal spaces. Then put any number from 1 to 9 in each of these spaces.* Demonstrate how to spin. *Place the spinner over the outline and hold it still while you spin.*

PLAYING THE GAME

3 When children have made their spinners, have a volunteer help you show the class how to play the game. Then let pairs play the game on their own.

4 At the end of math time, discuss the game.

- *How did you decide on the sum you chose?*

- *Did anything surprising happen with your spinners?*

Along with being fun, this game is about sample space. In order for children to determine which sum is more likely to come up, the first step they must be able to take is to know which sums actually are possible. This game helps them take that first step.

That's two times for my sum, so I win.

Giving Directions

Is it hard to write the directions for playing a probability game?

THINKING ABOUT DIRECTIONS

1 Begin by finding out what children already know about directions.

- *What are some things people use directions for?*
- *What things have you used directions for?*
- *What are some things the directions told you?*

2 Pass out the directions you've collected. **With your partner (or group), look at these directions and talk about what you notice. There are probably many things you can figure out without reading all the words.** After children have studied the directions, discuss what they've observed.

- *What are your directions about? How do you know?* (the title says, from the pictures)
- *What are some things your directions include?* (pictures, numbered steps, what you need, how many players, words telling you how to play)
- *Could you follow these directions?*

WRITING DIRECTIONS

Two people can play and they each need a spinner and a pencil and paper.

3 *During math time, you and your partner played a game called* **Spin a Sum.** Ask for volunteers to review the rules of the game.

4 *Today you will be writing directions for the game so you can play it at home.* Have the children offer suggestions for what to include in the directions, then write independently.

> Though the children are writing independently, encourage conversations among them as they work. Sharing ideas and talking about approaches are aspects of a rich classroom environment that supports children working on challenging tasks.

REVISING DIRECTIONS

5 When the children are finished writing their directions, have them take turns reading their writing to a partner.

- *Are the directions clear? If not, tell your partner what you can't understand.*

- *Would another illustration be helpful?*

- *Can you figure out how to play the game by following the directions?*

LET'S PLAY!

6 Have the children take their spinners and directions home to play the game with family members. A day or two later, invite the children to share how well their written directions explained the game to family members.

ASSESSMENT

To assess this writing activity, evaluate how well the children communicate the directions to *Spin a Sum*.

- *Did the child write clear and complete directions?*

- *Did the child include illustrations that helped to clarify the written directions?*

(Classroom Talk)

INTERVIEWS AS A MEANS OF EVALUATION

The best kind of evaluation is an ongoing conversation between teacher and child. For the child, this type of evaluation helps demonstrate and clarify understandings. For the teacher, evaluation provides information that helps structure learning experiences. Whereas answers alone on a page often reveal little about the thinking involved in solving problems, interviews of children are opportunities to investigate children's understandings and misconceptions.

TEN FRAME

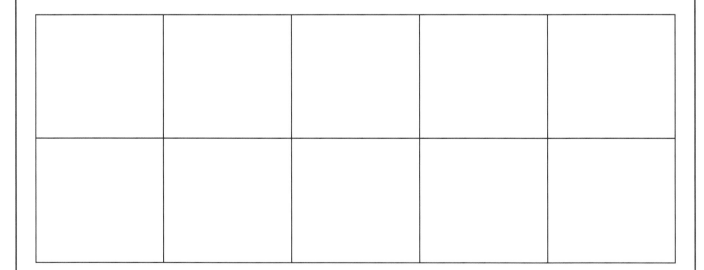

HUNDRED NUMBER BOARD SECTIONS

1	2	3	4	5
11	12	13	14	15
21	22	23	24	25
31	32	33	34	35
41	42	43	44	45

To the teacher: Permission is granted to reproduce this page.

HUNDRED NUMBER BOARD SECTIONS

6	7	8	9	10
16	17	18	19	20
26	27	28	29	30
36	37	38	39	40
46	47	48	49	50

HUNDRED NUMBER BOARD SECTIONS

51	52	53	54	55
61	62	63	64	65
71	72	73	74	75
81	82	83	84	85
91	92	93	94	95

HUNDRED NUMBER BOARD SECTIONS

56	57	58	59	60
66	67	68	69	70
76	77	78	79	80
86	87	88	89	90
96	97	98	99	100

To the teacher: Permission is granted to reproduce this page.

Dear Family,

This week in math we've been exploring the numbers 1 to 100. To extend this learning experience, the children have written letters to explain how they sequenced a list of numbers. Please take the time to read the attached letter and write back to your child. Have your child bring your response back to school to be shared with the class.

      Thank you,

_____